Thank You,
HEROES

For Captain Tom, a true hero
~ P.H.

For Noah and Matilda
~ M.E.

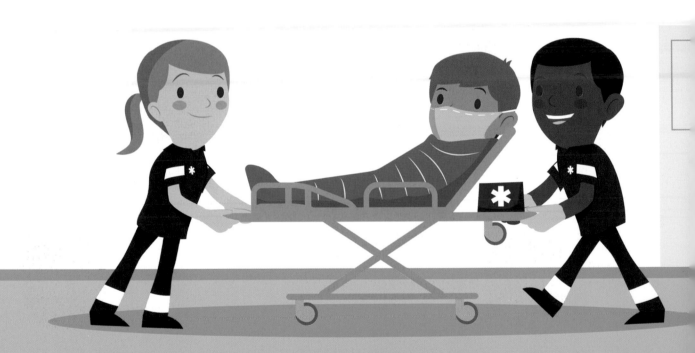

CATERPILLAR BOOKS
An imprint of the Little Tiger Group
www.littletiger.co.uk
1 Coda Studios, 189 Munster Road, London SW6 6AW
First published in Great Britain 2020
Text by Patricia Hegarty • Text copyright © Caterpillar Books Ltd 2020
Illustrations copyright © Michael Emmerson 2020
A CIP catalogue record for this book is available from the British Library
All rights reserved • Printed in Latvia
ISBN: 978-1-83891-191-1 • LTP/5000/3411/0620
2 4 6 8 10 9 7 5 3 1

Thank You,
HEROES

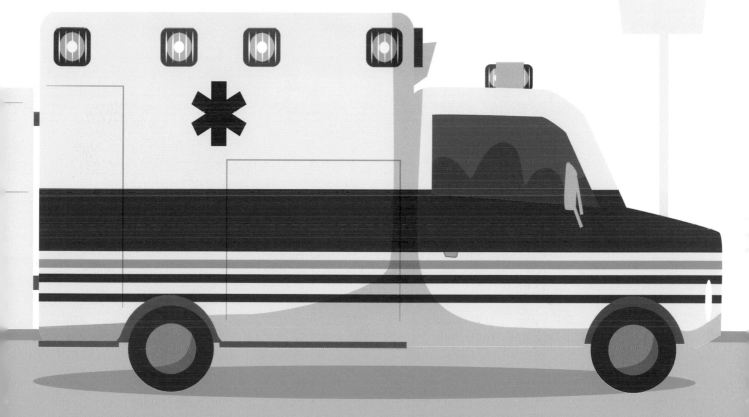

By Patricia Hegarty

Illustrated by Michael Emmerson

LITTLE TIGER

LONDON

The world is full of

HEROES,

and when
the going gets

tough,

Those heroes
all get going,

we can't
thank them enough!

Three cheers for the **DOCTORS,** keeping **viruses** at bay,

You are **heroes**, yes, you are,

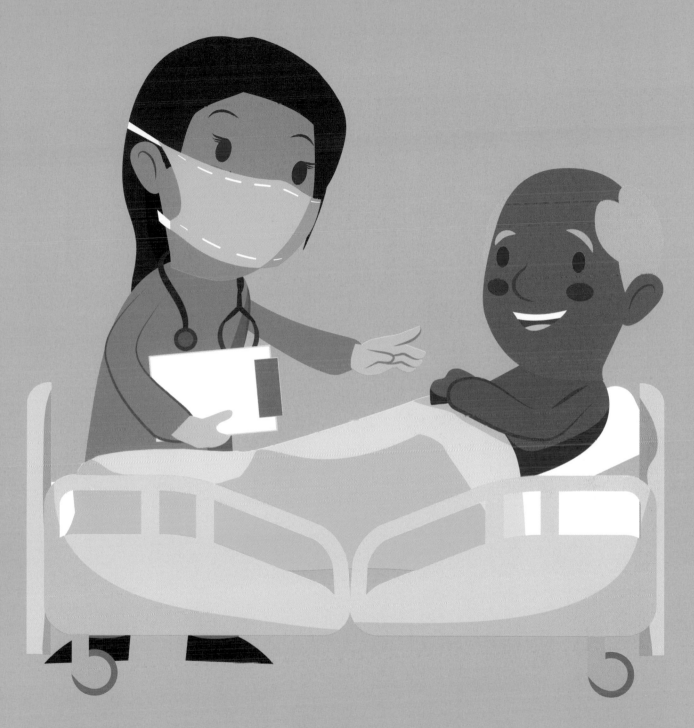

hip-hip-hip-hurray!

Let's hear it FOR THE
NURSES,
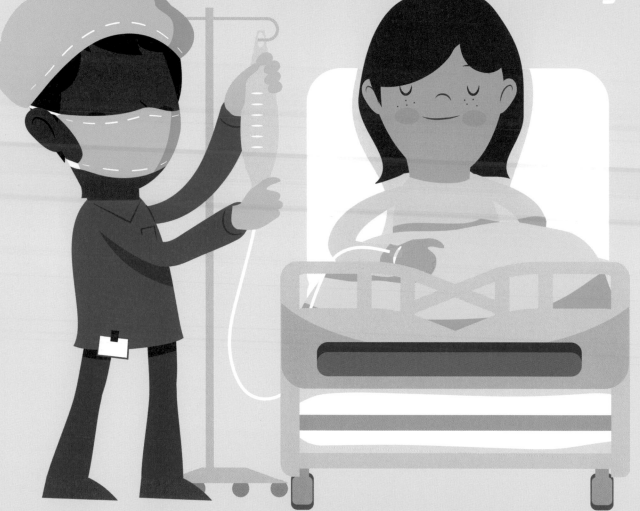
tending patients
all day long.

You are **heroes,**
yes, you are,

you're
kind
and **brave**
and
strong!

Here's to PARAMEDICS,

who **save** so **many** lives.

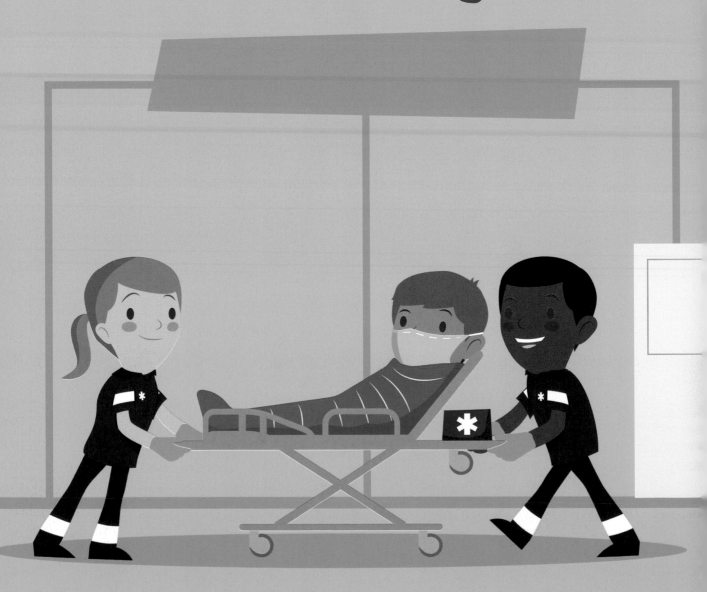

You are **heroes,**
yes, you are,

we're sending you
high fives!

To each
HOSPITAL WORKER,

for
everything you do,

You are **heroes,**

yes,
you are,

we **OWE** our
thanks to **you!**

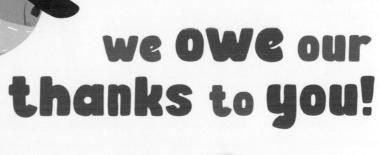

To the
CARERS
everywhere,

as you all
play your parts,

You are **heroes**, yes, you are,
we keep you in **our hearts!**

We salute
DELIVERY
PEOPLE
all across the land.

You are heroes,
yes, you are,

and you
deserve
a
hand!

Thumbs up to all the WORKERS

who sort the **bins** and **mail**,

You are **heroes,**
yes, you are,

and you never,
ever fail!

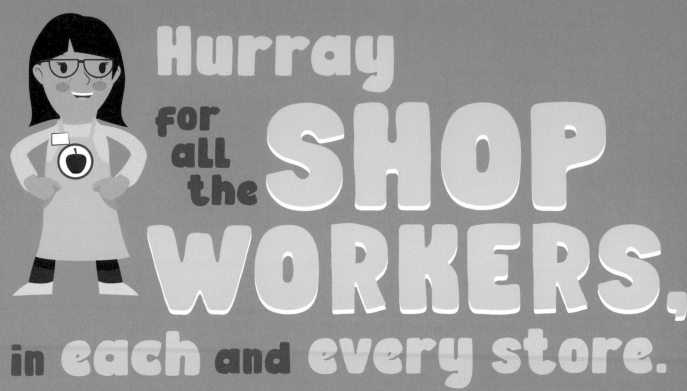

Hurray for all the SHOP WORKERS, in each and every store.

You are heroes, yes, you are,

we couldn't
love you more!

Let's **not forget** the **TEACHERS,** in **classrooms** and **online.**

You are **heroes,**
yes, you are,

you
help
young minds to
shine!

You are **heroes,**
yes, you are,

on that
we all
agree!

We're **PROUD** of all our **HEROES**, so we **CLAP** and **make** a din.

We're all in this together, and together we will win!

Meet Some
HEROES

Doctors work out what is wrong with us when we are sick and give prescriptions to help us get better.

Nurses work hard to care for us and make sure we get the medicine and help we need.

Paramedics are on the front line, responding to emergencies, driving ambulances and saving lives.

Warehouse workers handle the safe packing and delivery of millions of goods from all around the world to our shops and homes.

All the **staff in hospitals** have an important role to play, from the kitchen staff to the porters and the cleaners.

There are millions of **carers** looking after our loved ones, in nursing homes and in their own homes.

Delivery workers travel far and wide to make sure we all have the things we need.

Volunteers help in the community by delivering food, helping neighbours and fundraising.

Shop workers
keep the shelves stocked in stores with food and everyday supplies.

Teachers carry
on with their lessons in classrooms or online so we can all keep learning.

Our transport workers drive buses
and trains so we can get to where we need to be.